# UNITS 1, 2, 3

ISBN 978-1-60218-550-0
ISBN 1-60218-550-6
167249

12  11  10  09          3  4  5  6

**Sopris West®**
EDUCATIONAL SERVICES

A Cambium Learning®Company

BOSTON, MA · LONGMONT, CO

# UNIT 1 • Maya and Ben

# UNIT 3 • African Adventures

# UNIT 1
# Maya and Ben

# A Perfect Year

*by Ms. Mak*

*illustrated by Jana Christy*

What is the title of the story? If you could have a perfect year, what would it be like?

# Vocabulary

## ★ per·fect

When something is **perfect**, it is so good that it cannot get any better.

My birthday party was *perfect*. Everything was just the way I dreamed it would be. What would your perfect birthday party be like?

## ★ re·spect

When you have **respect** for someone, you like the things they do or say. You think highly of that person.

The children at our school have *respect* for the principal. Children should show respect to their parents and their teachers. Who do you respect?

★ = New

## ★ in·ven·tor

An **inventor** is someone who makes or thinks of something new to use.

Benjamin Franklin was the *inventor* of the first lightning rod.

Thomas Edison was the inventor of the first light bulbs that could be used by many people.

The Wright brothers were inventors of the first airplane that flew. What were Benjamin Franklin, Thomas Edison, and the Wright brothers?

## ★ plain

Something **plain** is simple or ordinary.

I have a *plain* T-shirt. It is white with nothing on it. What makes my T-shirt plain?

## ★ scowl

When you **scowl**, you make a face that shows you are mad or unhappy.

Meg *scowled* when she realized her lunchbox was broken. Show me how you scowl.

**Chapter 1**

# Mighty Maya

Who is the chapter about? Why do you think she is called Mighty Maya?

Grade 2, Room 7, Maya M. Martinez

Hi, my name is Maya. I'm seven years old, and I'm in second grade.

Second grade was going to be the perfect year. I have the perfect teacher. His name is Mr. Chapman. He gets a lot of respect. He plays drums when we sing, and he is always doing cool science stuff.

I have the perfect classroom. It's near the playground.

I sit at the perfect desk. It's next to the fish tank with the eel.

I even have perfect hair! My best friend, Ana, and I braided beads into our hair.

I am on the perfect soccer team. I am called Mighty Maya because I am the star kicker on the team.

Why was second grade going to be a *perfect* year for Maya? Who is Maya's teacher? Why does he get *respect* from his students?

Everything was perfect until last Wednesday. It was 10:00 a.m., way after the tardy bell rang, when this kid with spiky hair and glasses walked in. He was no ordinary kid.

What happened at 10:00 a.m.? What do you think the new kid will do?

Mr. Chapman said, "Class, I would like you to meet Benjamin Franklin Thomas Edison Wright."

I thought to myself, "What kind of name is that? This kid must think he's cool!"

Then things went from bad to worse. Mr. Chapman sat Benjamin Edison Franklin . . . whatever . . . in the chair right next to me! Yuck!

I sighed, "So much for a perfect year."

Why did Maya think that Benjamin Franklin Thomas Edison Wright was no *ordinary* kid? What is Maya's problem?

## Chapter 2

# Just Plain Ben

What's the title of the chapter? What do you think you know about Ben so far?

Grade 2, Room 7,  Benjamin F.T.E. Wright

Hi, my name is Ben. I'm seven years old, and I'm in second grade. My dad and I just moved to the Bronx. Another school (my sixth), another teacher (my sixth), another class (my sixth), another desk (my sixth). I've lived all over the world, but I hoped that this would be the last move for us.

My teacher, Mr. Chapman, said, "Class, I would like you to meet Benjamin Franklin Thomas Edison Wright. Benjamin is named after not one, but *three* inventors. Ben's dad is a very important computer scientist."

How many schools has Ben attended? Do you think this will be the last move for him?

*worksheet*

I thought to myself, "So much for the perfect school. I wish I was just plain Ben Wright."

I looked around. The girl with the beads in her hair scowled when Mr. Chapman said that I had lived all around the world. I thought, "I wish I was just plain Ben Wright who had never moved and never lived anywhere but the Bronx."

Then things went from bad to worse. Mr. Chapman sat me right next to the girl with the beads in her hair. Yuck!

Why do you think Ben wished he was just *plain* Ben? What is Ben's problem?

## Chapters 3, 4

# Vocabulary

## per·fect

When something is **perfect**, it is so good that it cannot get any better.

Maya and Ben each wanted a *perfect* second grade year. What do you think would make a perfect second grade year?

## plain

Something **plain** is simple or ordinary.

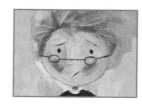

Benjamin wanted others to call him just *plain* Ben. Why?

## ★ pout

When you **pout**, you push out your lower lip to show that you are unhappy.

Maya wanted to stay up late. Her mom said no, so she got upset and *pouted*.

Show me what you would look like if you were pouting.

## ★ = New

## ★ speech·less

If you are so surprised you can't think of what to say, you are **speechless**.

Maya was so surprised to get a bike for her birthday that she was *speechless*. What did she say?

## ★ a·mazed

When you are **amazed**, you are surprised, often in a good way.

I was *amazed* when my friend rode a big horse. Why was I amazed?

**Chapter 3**

# No Ordinary Room

In Apartment 9B, Maya sat pouting. Maya's mom said, "Hey, Moody Maya, please go get your little brother. He's playing downstairs with the boy in Apartment 8B. The family just moved in."

In Apartment 8B, the doorbell buzzed. Bzzz, bzzz. Ben pulled himself off the couch. He shuffled across the floor and opened the door. Ben and Maya stood there speechless, glaring at each other.

Then at exactly the same time, Maya and Ben shouted, "What are you doing here?"

Ben said, "What do you mean? I live here."

Where do Ben and Maya live? Why did Maya go to Ben's apartment? Why were Ben and Maya *speechless*? What do you think will happen next?

Just then Maya's little brother, BJ, came bounding from another room. BJ tugged at Maya, "Come see the computer room!"

Maya hesitated. Then she went with BJ into the other room. Ben's little brother sat at one computer, and a man with big round glasses and spiky hair sat at another computer.

Maya's mouth dropped open. She was amazed. This was no ordinary room. One, two, three, four, five . . . There were five computers in the room!

Where did Maya's little brother take her? Why was Maya *amazed*?

Without stopping to think, Maya blurted, "Wow! Way cool! Way cool, Benjamin, Edison, Wright, Jones, or whoever you are."

Ben said, "I'm Ben, just plain Ben."

What did Maya learn about Ben?

**Chapter 4**

# Earth on the Web

What do you think this chapter will be about?

Ben's dad didn't look up from the computer.
Ben's dad typed—click, click, click.

The screen went black. Little stars appeared.
"Whooooosh," said Maya as the screen zoomed
in on Earth. "Look at that! It's Earth." Maya
was amazed.

Look at the computer screen. Why was Maya amazed?

Click, click, click. Ben's dad typed an address. Whoosh! The Earth turned. The camera zoomed in. Maya exclaimed, "It's North America! There's the United States."

"Look, we're zooming in on the city," Maya blurted. "There's the Bronx. Wow! There's our apartment building!"

Ben said, "Wow, it's just like being a bird in the sky. Check that out."

The kids crowded around the computer screen.

Why did Ben say it's like being a bird in the sky? Why did the kids crowd around the computer?

Ben said, "We just got back from England. Can we go to England on the computer?"

Ben's dad scratched his head and started to type into the computer when the doorbell buzzed.

"Oh," said Maya. "I bet it's Mom."

Ben and Maya went to the door. Maya's mom asked, "What are you doing?"

Maya said, "Sorry, Mom. This is Ben—my friend Ben—just plain Ben."

What did the kids see on the Internet site? Why did Maya introduce Ben as "just plain Ben"? What do you think Maya and Ben will do in the next chapter?

**Chapter 5**

# Vocabulary

### in·ven·tor

An **inventor** is someone who makes or thinks of something new to use.

Who was Ben named after? What did Benjamin Franklin, Thomas Edison, and the Wright brothers do?

### pout

When you **pout**, you push out your lower lip to show that you are unhappy.

Maya *pouted* when Ben joined her class. Why did she pout?

### speech·less

If you are so surprised you can't think of what to say, you are **speechless**.

Maya and Ben were *speechless* when they saw each other at the door of the apartment. What did they say?

★ = New

## a·mazed

When you are **amazed**, you are surprised, often in a good way.

Maya was *amazed* by the Internet pictures and maps. What amazed Maya?

## ★ get car·ried a·way

If you **get carried away** with something, you do more than you had planned.

Maya and her mom went shopping. They *got carried away* and bought seven bags of groceries. What did Maya and her mom get carried away with? How could you tell they got carried away?

 **Chapter 5**

# Perfect or What?

Do you think second grade is going to be perfect for Ben and Maya?

It's me, Maya, again. Ben, Ana, and I all hang out together now. Ana and I still have beads braided into our hair. Ben still has spiky hair, and we all get along.

We all play soccer. My mom helped Ben learn how to dribble the ball.

Sometimes we go to Ana's. She has a yard that we can play in.

Sometimes we hang out at Ben's. He's got all the cool computers.

Who are the friends in this chapter? What do they like to do together?

The three of us like to work on projects together. Mr. Chapman is teaching us about maps.

On Saturday morning, Ana, Ben, and I met to work on a map project. We needed to do only one map, but we got carried away.

Ana, Ben, and Maya *got carried away* with their map project. What do you think they did?

By 4:00 p.m., we had munched through a bag of banana chips, three apples, and six cheese sticks. We had used up a box of crayons. We ended up with maps of:

1. Our planet, Earth

2. Our continent, North America

3. Our country, the United States

Amazing! Are we good or what? Perfect project. Perfect snacks. Perfect friends.

Second grade is perfect after all!

What did the kids make maps of? How did Maya's second grade year turn out? How is that different from what she expected when she first met Ben?

# Story Retell

## A Perfect Year

We're going to retell the story.
What is the title of the story?

Who are the two main characters?

Where did the whole story take place?
(Hint: Where were the school and the
children's homes located?)

---

● At the beginning of the story,
what did you learn about Maya?
What did you learn about Ben?

---

■ What happened in the middle of the
story when Maya went to pick up her
little brother?

---

▲ What happened at the end of
the story?

# Fluency

## Eel in the Fish Tank
*by Paula Rich*

My name is Eel.  I live in the fish tank in     11
Mr. Chapman's second grade classroom.  Every     17
school day, a girl with beads in her hair sits at     28
the desk next to me.  She's cool.  She talks to     38
me softly.  She never taps on the glass, and she     48
scowls at kids who do.  Best of all, she feeds me.     59

I'm glad she's the eel feeder.  I hope she     68
gets to keep her job all year.  Last year, I almost     79
starved because the eel feeder forgot.  Then     86
another eel feeder gave me too much food, and     95
I got sick.  The girl with beads in her hair gives     106
me just the right amount.     111

Some of the kids are frightened of me.  I'm     120
big and slimy, and I have lots of sharp teeth.  I     131
open and close my mouth all the time, but that's     141
just the way I breathe.  The girl with beads in     151
her hair understands me.  She's not scared.  She     159
gives me respect.     162

Who is telling the story?  Who is the girl with the beads?  Why does
Eel like her?

# UNIT 2
# Mapping Our World

# A Bird's-Eye View

*by Ms. Mak*

*illustrated by Jana Christy*

Look at the picture. Imagine you are the bird flying over this neighborhood. What do you see below you?

## Chapters 1, 2

# Vocabulary

★ **plan·et**

A **planet** is a large ball that circles a star. The Earth is a planet.

Earth circles a star—our Sun. What is Earth?

★ **globe**

A **globe** is a map of the world shaped like the Earth.

We found where we live on the *globe*. Can you find where you live?

★ **con·ti·nent**

A **continent** is one of seven large land areas on Earth.

The United States is on the *continent* of North America. Do you live on a continent? If yes, what continent do you live on?

★ = New

## ★ neigh·bor·hood

A **neighborhood** is a part of a town. It is made up of people who live near each other.

Every *neighborhood* is different.
This is my neighborhood.
What's in your neighborhood?

## ★ vast

A place that is **vast** is very great in size. It is enormous.

The ocean is enormous.
It is . . .

**Idioms and Expressions**

## get car·ried a·way

If you **get carried away** with something, you do more than you had planned.

Maya, Ben, and Ana needed only one map for their project. How did you know they *got carried away* with their map project?

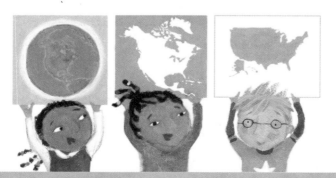

**Chapter 1**

# Our World

**Our Planet**

Earth is my home and yours too. We all share the planet Earth.

When we walk on Earth, everything seems flat. However, Earth is really round.

A globe is a round map shaped like the Earth. A globe is a great way to show what Earth looks like.

Planet Earth                    Globe

What is Earth? What is a *globe?*

Most maps that we draw are flat maps. Most flat maps are drawings of smaller parts of the Earth—the continents, islands, countries, and states. We can draw maps of our neighborhoods, buildings, and even our homes.

### Earth
by Ben, Maya, and Ana

This is the planet we live on.

Earth is our home. It is like a big round ball.

**Our Continents**

Continents are vast areas of land. There are seven continents in the world. Most of you live on the continent of North America.

### North America
by Ben, Maya, and Ana

This is the continent we live on. It is called North America. It is vast. (That's a snazzy word for very, very big.)

P.S. If you live on an island, you do not live on a continent. Islands are much smaller than continents.

What is a *continent*? What continent do Ben, Maya, and Ana live on? Do you live on a continent or an island?

35

## Our Countries

A country can be big or small. There are about 192 countries in the world.

What country do you live in? Many of you live in the United States, but some of you may live in Canada, or perhaps even on the island country of Samoa.

### The United States
by Ben, Maya, and Ana
This is the country we live in.
It is called the United States.

P.S. If you live in the United States, you live with about 300 million people!

You and other readers share the Earth and perhaps a continent and a country. Are we perfect or what?

Why does Maya think we are perfect?

**Chapter 2**

# Our Neighborhoods, Our Homes

### Ana, Ben, and Maya's Neighborhood

We can make maps of our world, our continents, and our countries. We can also make maps of smaller places, like our neighborhoods. A map is like what a bird would see if it looked down from the sky. This is a bird's-eye view of the kids' neighborhood.

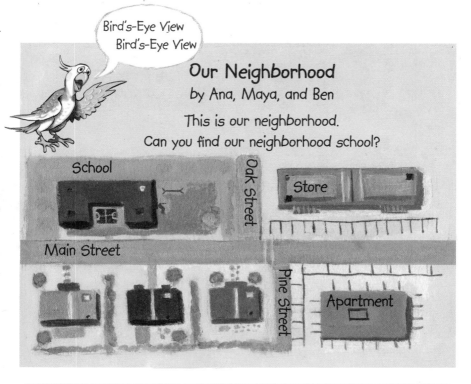

What does this map show? Why is it called a *bird's-eye view*?

## Ana's House

This is a bird's-eye view of Ana's house.

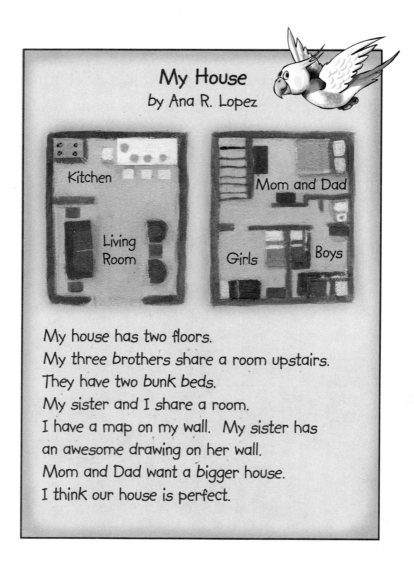

My House
by Ana R. Lopez

Kitchen

Mom and Dad

Living
Room

Girls

Boys

My house has two floors.
My three brothers share a room upstairs.
They have two bunk beds.
My sister and I share a room.
I have a map on my wall. My sister has
an awesome drawing on her wall.
Mom and Dad want a bigger house.
I think our house is perfect.

What is this a map of? What do you know about Ana's house?

## Maya's Apartment

This is a bird's-eye view of Maya's apartment.

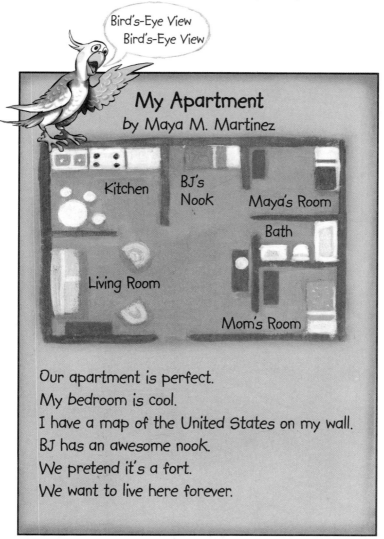

Bird's-Eye View
Bird's-Eye View

### My Apartment
by Maya M. Martinez

Kitchen

BJ's Nook

Maya's Room

Bath

Living Room

Mom's Room

Our apartment is perfect.
My bedroom is cool.
I have a map of the United States on my wall.
BJ has an awesome nook.
We pretend it's a fort.
We want to live here forever.

Describe Maya's apartment.

## Ben's Apartment

Ben and Maya live in the same apartment building.

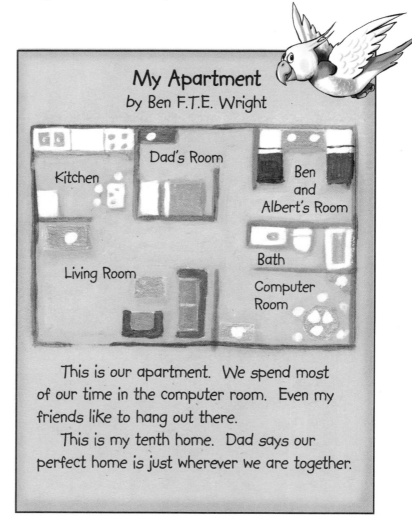

## My Apartment
### by Ben F.T.E. Wright

Kitchen

Dad's Room

Ben and Albert's Room

Living Room

Bath

Computer Room

This is our apartment. We spend most of our time in the computer room. Even my friends like to hang out there.

This is my tenth home. Dad says our perfect home is just wherever we are together.

Ben has gone to six schools. Why is this his tenth home?

**Our Maps**

Hi, it's me, Mr. Chapman. Look at the maps my class made. Each map is perfect! Are we good or what?

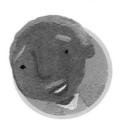

How can you tell Mr. Chapman is proud of his class? How do you think the kids feel about their work?

# People on the Move

*by Jessica Sprick, Marilyn Sprick,*
*Ann Watanabe, and Karen Akiyama-Paik*
*illustrated by Jana Christy*

Look at the family. What are they doing? Where do you think they are going?

**Chapters 1–3**

# Vocabulary

## ★ im·mi·grant

A person who moves from one country to another is called an **immigrant**.

People who move from England to the United States are . . . People who move from the United States to Canada are . . .

## ★ re·la·tive

A **relative** is a person who is part of your family. Relatives are people who were born, adopted, or married into your family.

Our *relatives* all came to my sister's wedding. My cousins, aunts, and uncles came from far away to join us. Name some of your relatives.

## ★ cram

**Cram** means to stuff things or people into small places.

We *crammed* our clothes into the suitcase. It was so packed, we could barely close it. Look at the picture. What are the kids doing?

★ = New

## ★ be·long·ings

**Belongings** are things that you own. They belong to you.

Sam packed his *belongings* in his backpack. He was sleeping over at Grandpa's house. What do you think Sam packed?

## ★ tra·di·tion

A **tradition** is a belief or a way of doing something that families pass on to their children.

In some families, it is a *tradition* to eat turkey on Thanksgiving Day. Do you have any special traditions on Valentine's Day?

**Chapter 1**

# Oodles and Caboodles

Wrap it, stack it, stuff it in a box!
Piles of clothes, stacks of dishes,
Hundreds of pictures,
Dozens of books,
Oodles and caboodles
Of jam-packed boxes.

Pack it, stack it, squeeze it tight!
Boxes, suitcases, skates, and bikes,
Couches, beds, tables, and chairs,
Oodles and caboodles of important stuff.
It's moving day!

Have you ever moved? Where did you live? What was it like to pack all your *belongings*?

People come and people go. People are always on the move. They move from one place to another—over land and sea, by train, plane, bus, and car. Sometimes even on foot.

Think about packing everything you have and moving it to a new place. Could you really take everything? How many boxes would you need? Could you send it by plane? Could you pack it in your car? Could you carry everything you have on your back?

People are moving all the time. Did you know that many families move one time every five years? That takes oodles and caboodles of boxes! Packing all your belongings is a lot of work.

How often do many families move? Why do you think they move?

Why do people move?
Sometimes people have to move.
Sometimes people choose to move.

People move to start a job, to be near family, or just to have an adventure. Most people move to find a better life.

## The Wrights on the Move

I've been offered a job on a dino dig.

What do you think?

Awesome! A dinosaur dig! Let's get packing.

Here's a box.

Name some reasons why people move. Look at the picture. Why are Ben and his family moving again? Do you think moving is *bittersweet* for Ben? Why or why not?

# From Here to There

If you live in the United States, you've probably moved at least one time. You may have moved a few blocks, all the way across town, or to a different state. You may have traveled by car, bus, train, plane, or even in a ship.

**From Country to Country**

Some people move from one country to another. These people are called immigrants. You, your parents, your grandparents, your great-grandparents, or even your great-great-grandparents may have come to America from another country.

---

When people move from country to country, what are they called?

## The Earliest Americans

Thousands of years ago, there weren't any people in America. Some scientists think that the first people came to our continent about 14,000 years ago. They came looking for food. These people may have walked from Asia to America on a strip of land that no longer exists.

Think about walking and carrying all your belongings for months at a time!

How do some scientists think the first *immigrants* came to America? What do you think this trip would have been like?

## Immigrants 200 Years Ago

Before there were planes and cars, immigrating to any country was very hard. People walked. They rode on animals. They rode in carts and covered wagons pulled by animals.

Many immigrants traveled by boat. Men, women, and children were often crammed into small spaces for weeks at a time. Many immigrants had to leave most of their belongings behind.

Imagine moving all your belongings in a crowded boat.

Describe what you think it would have been like to travel for weeks on a crowded boat. What would you have done to pass the time?

## Immigrants Today

Today, people are still moving to America. People come by boat, but they also travel by car, bus, train, and plane. Has anyone in your class moved from another country? Is anyone from Spain, Mexico, Japan, or Ghana? Where are you or your relatives from?

Today some people immigrate to another country by plane.

Name some ways people immigrate today. Which way would you choose to travel? Why?

Over hundreds of years, immigrants have shared their colorful customs, tasty foods, and the rich sounds of many languages.

America is a wonderful mix of people and traditions from places all around the world.

More than 300 languages are spoken in the United States.

**Family Stories**

Everyone has a story to tell about his or her family's history. The story may involve a move, even if it was way back in time.

My great-grandparents came to the United States from Panama.

What is your family's history?

## Chapter 3

# Maya's Story

Maya is going to tell a story about her family's history. Family histories almost always involve a . . . move.

Maya Martinez stood in front of the class clutching a small wooden box. "I have something very cool from my great-great-great-great-great-granddad," Maya said as she carefully counted the "greats" on her fingers.

Maya slowly opened the box. The class was absolutely still. Maya pulled out a faded red bandana. "My super-great-granddad was a cowboy," said Maya. Then she added, "This is his bandana. It is old, old, old.

"Mama says my super-great-granddad was a slave. His father was stolen from Africa. They put him in a big boat and brought him across the ocean. I don't think my super-great-granddad's father wanted to come. The slave traders made him move."

Maya said that her super-great-granddad's father was brought here from Africa. How did he get to the United States? Was it right for the slave traders to steal him from Africa? Maya has an interesting family story.

"When my super-great-granddad became a free man, he was very happy. He became a cowboy. I'm going to write my story about the bandana and how my super-great-granddad went on a cattle drive."

The class asked Maya questions. Maya wasn't sure how to answer many of them, but she got a lot of ideas for her story.

All of the kids in Mr. Chapman's class had brought something to write about. Emily had a purple button, Jason had a pebble, Alison had a bent straw, and Betsy had an old woolen shawl. Soon everyone was busy drawing and writing. There would be many interesting stories to read.

Why do you think Maya's super-great-granddad was happy being a cowboy? Do you have something that used to belong to your parents or grandparents? What does it tell you about your *relatives*?

# Fluency

## That Kind of Day

*by Jessica Sprick and Ms. Mak*
*illustrated by Jana Christy*

It was a perfect year, until Maya got an e-mail from her friend Ben.  Maya stomped around the apartment, muttering to herself.  Then she sat down and wrote a poem.

### A Yucky, Yucky Day

It's been that kind of day,    6
A yucky sort of day.    11
Nothing, absolutely nothing,    14
Nothing's gone my way!    18

Got mud on my new shirt,    24
I stained my birthday shirt.    29
Awful, absolutely awful,    32
As bad as eating dirt!    37

Mom packed a yummy lunch,    42
My favorite-ever lunch.    46
Yucky, absolutely yucky,    49
To find a bug to munch!    55

# Fluency

The soccer game was on,                5
The kick was mine or gone.             11
Shocking, absolutely shocking,         14
To find my face on the lawn!           21

My bestest friend is Ben,              26
Funny, just plain Ben.                 30
Awful, absolutely awful,               33
He's on the move again!                38

It's been that kind of day,            44
A yucky sort of day.                   49
Nothing, absolutely nothing,           52
Nothing's gone my way.                 56

Two weeks passed. Maya wrote a cool story about her super-great-grandfather. She got an A++. Maya hummed. Then she sat down and wrote a new poem.

## An Almost Perfect Day

It's an a-okay day,                                    5
An almost perfect day.                                 9
Many things, a lot of things,                         15
Have really gone my way!                              20

Mom packed a yummy lunch,                             25
My bestest-ever lunch.                                29
Yummy, truly yummy,                                   32
Drooling as I munch!                                  36

The corner kick was fine,                             41
A soccer game so fine.                                46
Perfect, truly perfect,                               49
That winning goal was mine!                           54

An e-mail from pal Ben,                               59
Funny, just plain Ben.                                63
Awesome, really awesome,                              66
Bones from way back when!                             71

It's been a super day,                                76
An almost perfect day.                                80
Many things, a lot of things,                         86
Have really gone my way!                              91

# UNIT 3
# African Adventures

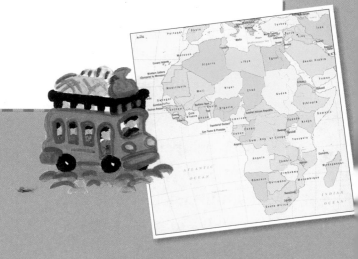

# Miss Tam in Africa

*by Jessica Sprick*

*illustrated by Paige Eastburn O'Rourke*

Who is this story about? Where does the story take place? Find Miss Tam.
What do you think she will do in this story?

# Vocabulary

★ **man·ners**

**Manners** are how you behave around other people. Manners can be good or bad.

In most places, it is good *manners* to wipe your mouth with a napkin. In most places, it is bad manners to wipe your mouth on your sleeve. What are some ways to show good manners in our culture?

★ **Af·ri·ca**

**Africa** is one of Earth's seven continents.

*Africa* is a huge continent. It is vast. Trace the continent of Africa with your finger.

★ = New

## ★ ad·ven·ture

An **adventure** is doing something or going somewhere new and exciting.

Sailing for the first time was a great *adventure*.

Have you ever been on an adventure? What was it?

## ★ stur·dy

**Sturdy** means strong, well-made, and not easily broken.

The house I built is very *sturdy*. Do you think my house will blow away in a wind storm? Why not?

## ★ Gha·na

**Ghana** (Gah-nuh) is a country in Western Africa.

Touch *Ghana* on the map.

**Chapter 1**

# Where to Go? What to See?

What do you think will happen in this chapter?

At exactly 6:30 a.m., Minnie Bird screeched, "Good morning!"

It had been Miss Tam's habit for 30 years to pop out of bed, put on her slippers, and put on her robe. However, this morning was different. It was not an ordinary day. Miss Tam was not going to work. She had retired. Miss Tam yawned and said, "I think I will sleep in."

What is Miss Tam doing? Why?

As was his habit, Old Scraggly Cat opened one eye and closed it again.

Finally, at exactly 7:00 a.m., Minnie Bird screeched, "Please, wake up! Seeds, please."

No, it was not an ordinary day. Miss Tam was sleeping late. Miss Tam opened one eye and smiled. "Minnie Bird, what good manners you have."

After breakfast, Miss Tam took out *Toot and Puddle* and 10 books about Africa.

"It's time to plan my first grand adventure," said Miss Tam.

Why does Miss Tam think Minnie Bird has good *manners*? Why isn't it an ordinary day? Look at the picture. What is Miss Tam doing?

Miss Tam carefully unfolded a world map and taped it to the wall.

"Bird's-eye view.  Bird's-eye view," screeched Minnie Bird.

Miss Tam stared at the world map for a long time.  "I will go to Africa to see hippos," said Miss Tam.  "I'll send you postcards, just like Toot sent to Puddle."

Why did Minnie Bird screech, "Bird's-eye view"?  Use the word *adventure* and tell what Miss Tam wants to do.

**Chapter 2**

# The Dark Blue Hatpin

What does Miss Tam want to do?
I wonder why this chapter is called "The Dark Blue Hatpin."

The next day, Miss Tam went to visit her old friend Mr. Moffitt.

Miss Tam put on her sturdy brown walking shoes and walked three blocks to the bus stop. She reached the library in time to have lunch with Mr. Moffitt. It was like old times.

Miss Tam said, "I am going to Africa. I will send you postcards."

What is Miss Tam doing? Why is it like old times?

Mr. Moffitt said, "Oh my, Miss Tam, Africa is a very big continent. You must go to the country of Ghana. There, my dear friend Kwesi (Kwe-see) will welcome you. He will take you to see amazing things!"

When Miss Tam got home, she took out a dark blue hatpin and stuck it into the country of Ghana. "I am going to Ghana, Minnie Bird."

Old Scraggly Cat crawled under the couch and pouted.

Why is this chapter called "The Dark Blue Hatpin"? Where is Miss Tam going to go? What did Old Scraggly Cat do?

"Don't worry. Mr. Moffitt will take good care of you while I am away," said Miss Tam.

Soon Miss Tam's new travel bag was packed. With a tear in her eye, she said goodbye to her friends. Parting was bittersweet.

A day and a half later, a stiff and tired Miss Tam toddled off the plane into a sea of people. She was in Ghana!

Why was parting bittersweet? Why was Miss Tam stiff and tired when she toddled off the plane in *Ghana*? Who can show me how to toddle? Let's all try it.

**Chapters 3, 4**

# Vocabulary

★ **in·sult**

An **insult** is something that you say or do that upsets another person.

In some countries, it is a custom to bow when you meet someone. If you don't bow, it's an . . .

★ **cus·tom**

A **custom** is a way of doing something. Often a group of people shares the same customs.

For some people, it is a *custom* to take off their shoes before they go into a house. For some people, it is a custom to shake hands when they meet.

Turn to the person next to you and shake his or her hand. Shaking hands is one of our . . .

★ **bar·gain**

When you **bargain**, you try to pay less for something than the seller's price.

In our culture, we sometimes *bargain* for a lower price at a garage sale.

When you want a lower price at a garage sale, you may . . .

★ = New

# ★ hab·i·tat

The place where an animal or plant lives and grows is called its **habitat**.

Some foxes live in the desert. What is their *habitat*?

# hes·i·tate

**Hesitate** means to stop before saying or doing something. You hesitate because you aren't sure what to do.

Miss Tam *hesitated* before she boarded the airplane. She wondered if this was the right flight.

Why do you think Miss Tam hesitated?

# ★ wild·life

Animals and plants that live in their natural habitat are called **wildlife**.

Many people study the forest *wildlife*.

Name some forest wildlife.

# ★ pro·tect·ed

When things, people, or animals are **protected**, they are kept safe from harm.

The animals in the wildlife park are *protected* from hunters.

Where else would you find animals that are protected?

## Chapter 3

# The Market

Where is Miss Tam? What do you think Miss Tam will do in this chapter?

The air was hot and still. Miss Tam was in Ghana! A tall thin man held up a paper that said, "Miss Tam." It was Mr. Moffitt's friend Kwesi. Miss Tam walked over to Kwesi.

Kwesi said, "Akwaaba (ah-kwah-bah), welcome."

What did Kwesi say to Miss Tam? What do you think *akwaaba* means?

Miss Tam held out her hand. She was careful to shake Kwesi's hand with her right hand. Miss Tam had learned that in Ghana it was good manners to use your right hand but an insult to shake someone's hand with your left.

Soon they were driving slowly in Kwesi's van. Miss Tam saw white buildings and palm trees from the window. She saw people in Western clothes and people in brightly printed African clothes.

"We must go to the market," Kwesi said. "There, you can see the food and crafts of my people."

At the market, Miss Tam was amazed by all the colors! As was the custom, Miss Tam bargained for a colorful skirt, a blue shirt, and African sandals.

"What fun!" exclaimed Miss Tam. She quickly took off her old shoes and put on her new African footwear.

---

How did Miss Tam show good manners? Describe what Miss Tam saw. What did she buy at the market?

The streets were filled with people. Women carried big baskets full of things on their heads. One woman walked by with a big bowl of eggs perfectly balanced on her head.

When Miss Tam got to her hotel room, she tried walking with her book bag on her head. She dropped it six times. It wasn't as easy as it looked!

What are some of the *customs* in Ghana? What did Miss Tam try? Was it easy? How do you think the women of Ghana learn to balance things on their heads?

## Chapter 4

# Hippos on the River

What has Miss Tam seen in Ghana so far?  What do you think she will do in this chapter?

That evening, Miss Tam ate a rice dish that was filled with meat, onions, tomatoes, and peppers. Rice in Ghana was different from the red beans and rice Miss Tam ate at home.

Kwesi arrived early the next morning.  "What do you want to see today?" he asked.

Miss Tam took *Toot and Puddle* from her bag and said, "I want to see hippos."

What did Miss Tam eat in Ghana?  How was it the same as eating at home? How was it different?  What did Miss Tam want to see?

Kwesi laughed. "Miss Tam, I have never seen a hippo in Ghana!" Kwesi hesitated, then said, "We will both have an adventure. We can go to a park where wildlife is protected. We might see the only hippos left in Ghana."

In the van, Miss Tam wrote a postcard.

After driving for many hours, Kwesi and Miss Tam arrived at the wildlife park. They hired a guide and rented a boat. Then they set off down the river to see some hippos.

What are Kwesi and Miss Tam doing? Why did Kwesi say, "We will both have an adventure"?

As they traveled on the river, Miss Tam looked into the forest. She spotted monkeys and colorful birds in the trees.

What did Miss Tam see on her river adventure?

Suddenly, Kwesi shouted, "Look! There!" Big gray lumps sat in the water. The guide said, "Hippos seem friendly, but they can be very mean. We must stay back."

To stay cool, the hippos waded in the mud and water. The guide said, "There used to be many hippos in Ghana. Now there are only a few hundred hippos because they have lost their habitat. If we are not careful, there will be no more hippos in Ghana."

Why do you think Kwesi had never seen a hippo before?

Kwesi and Miss Tam agreed that it would be very sad if there were no more hippos in Ghana.

Hippos are endangered. That means there are very few hippos left in the world.

**Chapter 5**

# Vocabulary

## ★ trick·ster

A **trickster** is someone who tricks or cheats others.

Many African stories have a *trickster* character named Anansi. This is a spider that tricks others. What is it called?

## ★ re·spect

To **respect** someone is to think highly of that person. If you respect someone, you treat that person well and listen to what that person says.

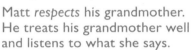

Matt *respects* his grandmother. He treats his grandmother well and listens to what she says.

What do you think Matt does when he is with his grandmother?

## ★ re·spect·ful·ly

When you respect someone, you treat them **respectfully**. You act in a way that shows respect for that person.

Matt treats his grandmother *respectfully*. He is very good to her and listens to her. How does Matt treat his grandmother?

★ = New

**Chapter 5**

# A Village Story

What do you think will happen in this chapter?

Soon it was time to go back. Kwesi said they would stop in a village to listen to a storyteller. Miss Tam could hardly wait.

In the village, Miss Tam sat under a tree with some kids and the old woman storyteller. The storyteller looked up at the sky and began to tell a story.

The tale had been passed from mother to daughter and father to son. There were no books and no pictures to look at.

Why is Miss Tam excited about listening to a storyteller?

As the old woman spoke, drummers played a different song for each animal and person in the story. Miss Tam listened carefully. The words and songs were beautiful.

Kwesi whispered, "The story is about a spider named Anansi." Miss Tam had read stories about this trickster to the children in Montgomery. Just like the children in Montgomery, the African children listened carefully and respectfully.

What is happening in the picture? Why do you think Kwesi told Miss Tam what was happening in the story?

When the old woman was done, Kwesi said, "The storyteller asked the children what they learned from her story."

A small boy said, "It is important to be honest."

"It is important to work hard," another boy said.

A girl said, "It is important to respect others."

"Children learn important lessons from storytellers!" Kwesi said with a grin.

Describe what happens during storytelling in Ghana. What did the children learn? Look at the picture. How can you tell the children listened *respectfully*?

Miss Tam's days in Ghana flew by. At the airport, Kwesi smiled and said, "I have a present for you. I wrote down the Anansi story so you can share it with the children in Montgomery."

With a tear in her eye, Miss Tam thanked Kwesi. While waiting for her plane, she sent an e-mail to her friends at the library.

From: Miss Tam
Date: June 1
To: Friends
Subject: Ghana

Dear Friends,

Ghana is amazing!

I went to the market and listened to a storyteller. Yesterday, I saw hippos in a wildlife park.

Love,
Miss Tam

Why do you think Miss Tam had a tear in her eye? Do you think going home was bittersweet for Miss Tam? Why?

# The River Horse

*by Paula Rich*

What do you see in the picture? Where do you think this story takes place?

**The River Horse**

# Vocabulary

★ **a·maz·ing**

Something that is **amazing** is surprising, often in a good way.

Walt is an *amazing* soccer player.

What kind of a player do you think Walt is?

**con·ti·nent**

A **continent** is a large area of land surrounded mostly by water. There are seven continents on Earth.

Miss Tam visited the *continent* of Africa.

Which continent is the country of Ghana on?

★ **her·bi·vore**

An **herbivore** is an animal that eats only plants.

A moose is an *herbivore* and eats grass, leaves, buds, and twigs.

What other things could an herbivore eat?

★ **graze**

**Graze** means to eat grass and leaves that are growing.

Horses *graze* in pastures most of the day. What other animals graze?

★ = New

There is something behind the curtain. What could it be?

**Clue #1:** It's as big as one small car but can weigh as much as two cars.

**Clue #2:** It's an animal. Two of its teeth can grow to 20 inches long.

**Clue #3:** It breathes air but is born underwater.

**Clue #4:** It can't swim but spends all day in the water.

What can it be?

What do you know about the animal behind the curtain? What do you think it is?

# What animal is this?

The amazing hippopotamus!

## A Hippo's Size

*Hippopotamus* is a big word that means river horse. Hippos are much bigger than horses though. They are only four to five feet tall, but they can weigh more than your family's car!

What does *hippopotamus* mean? Why is that a good name?

**A Hippo's Habitat**

Hippos live in Africa. They used to live all over the southern part of the continent. They lived wherever there was a river or lake and grass to eat. Now there are not so many hippos. They live mostly in wildlife parks, where they are protected from hunting.

Hippos live where it is hot. They spend all day in the water to keep cool. Often only the tips of their noses, ears, and eyes stick out of the water.

Describe a hippo's habitat? Why are they mostly found in *wildlife* parks now?

## A Hippo's Food

During the day, adult hippos walk on the river bottom and munch on underwater plants.

At night, hippos leave the water and graze on grass near the river. Hippos do not eat meat. They eat plants. Hippos are herbivores.

Adult hippos walk on the river bottom. Only baby hippos can swim.

Where do hippos eat? What do hippos eat? What makes a hippo an herbivore?

**Watch Out!**

Hippos are dangerous animals. They have long sharp teeth and big mouths. You could probably stand in a hippo's mouth when it's wide open! Hippos run faster than most people, so watch out. Don't get too close to a hippo!

A hippo's two biggest teeth may grow to be 20 inches long.

Why is it important to stay away from hippos? You've learned many facts about hippos. What makes them *amazing* animals?

# Glossary

## adventure

An **adventure** is doing something or going somewhere new and exciting.

Sailing for the first time was a great *adventure*.

## Africa

**Africa** is one of Earth's seven continents.

*Africa* is a large continent.

## amazed

When you are **amazed** you are surprised, often in a good way.

I was *amazed* when my friend rode a big horse.

My friend was *amazing*.

## bargain

When you **bargain**, you try to pay less for something than the seller's price.

In our culture, we sometimes *bargain* for a lower price at a garage sale.

## belongings

**Belongings** are things that you own. They belong to you.

We packed our *belongings* in suitcases.

## continent

A **continent** is a large area of land surrounded mostly by water. There are seven continents on Earth.

The United States is on the *continent* of North America.

## cram

**Cram** means to stuff things or people into small places.

We *crammed* our clothes into the suitcase. It was so packed, we could barely close it.

## custom

A **custom** is a way of doing something. Often a group of people shares the same customs.

Shaking hands is one of our *customs*.

## Ghana

**Ghana** (Gah-nuh) is a country in Western Africa.

Touch *Ghana* on the map.

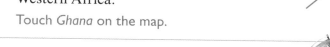

## globe

A **globe** is a map of the world shaped like the Earth.

We found where we live on the *globe*.

# Glossary

### graze

**Graze** means to eat grass and leaves that are growing.

Horses *graze* in pastures.

### habitat

The place where an animal or plant lives and grows is called its **habitat**.

Some foxes live in the desert. It is their *habitat*.

### herbivore

An **herbivore** is an animal that eats only plants.

A moose is an *herbivore* and eats grass, leaves, buds, and twigs.

### hesitate

**Hesitate** means to stop before saying or doing something. You hesitate because you aren't sure what to do.

The boy *hesitated* before he jumped off the diving board.

### immigrant

A person who moves from one country to another is called an **immigrant**.

*Immigrants* came to the United States from many other countries and found it very different from their homelands.

# insult

An **insult** is something that you say
or do that upsets another person.

In some countries, it is a custom to bow
when you meet someone. If you don't
bow, it's an *insult*.

# inventor

An **inventor** is someone who makes or
thinks of something new to use.

Thomas Edison was the *inventor* of light
bulbs that could be used by many people.

# manners

**Manners** are how you behave around
other people. Manners can be good
or bad.

In most places, it is good *manners* to
wipe your mouth with a napkin.

# neighborhood

A **neighborhood** is a part of a town.
It is made up of people who live near
each other.

Every *neighborhood* is different. This is
my neighborhood.

# perfect

When something is **perfect**, it is so
good that it cannot get any better.

The peach was *perfect*.

# Glossary

## plain

Something **plain** is simple or ordinary.

I have a *plain* T-shirt. It is white with nothing on it.

## planet

A **planet** is a large ball that circles a star. The Earth is a planet.

The *planet* Earth is our home.

## pout

When you **pout**, you push out your lower lip to show that you are unhappy.

The girl *pouted* when she didn't get her way.

## protected

When things, people, or animals are **protected**, they are kept safe from harm.

The animals in the wildlife park are *protected* from hunters.

## relative

A **relative** is a person who is part of your family. Relatives are people who were born, adopted, or married into your family.

Our *relatives* all came to the family reunion.

## respect

When you have **respect** for someone, you like the things they do or say. To respect someone is to think highly of that person.

Matt *respects* his grandmother. He treats his grandmother well.

## respectfully

When you respect someone, you treat them **respectfully**. You act in a way that shows respect for that person.

The class treats its teacher *respectfully*.

## scowl

When you **scowl**, you make a face that shows you are mad or unhappy.

The boy *scowled* because he was mad.

## speechless

If you are so surprised you can't think of what to say, you are **speechless**.

Maya and Ben were *speechless* when they saw each other at the door of the apartment.

## sturdy

**Sturdy** means strong, well-made, and not easily broken.

The shed was made of brick. It was very *sturdy*.

# Glossary

## tradition

A **tradition** is a belief or a way of doing something that families pass on to their children.

In many families, it is a *tradition* to eat turkey on Thanksgiving Day.

## trickster

A **trickster** is someone who tricks or cheats others.

Many African stories have a *trickster* character named Anansi. This is a spider that tricks others.

## vast

A place that is **vast** is very great in size. It is enormous.

Space is *vast*.

## wildlife

Animals and plants that live in their natural habitat are called **wildlife**.

Many people study the forest *wildlife*.

### Idioms and Expressions

## get carried away

If you **get carried away** with something, you do more than you had planned.

They *got carried away* and made many maps.